DENES AGAY'S LEARNING TO P[

EASY BOOGIE & [

Wise Publications
part of The Music Sales Group
London / New York / Paris / Sydney / Copenhagen / Berlin / Madrid / Tokyo

Published by
Wise Publications
14-15 Berners Street, London W1T 3LJ, UK

Exclusive Distributors:
Music Sales Limited
Distribution Centre, Newmarket Road,
Bury St Edmunds, Suffolk IP33 3YB, UK
Music Sales Pty Limited
20 Resolution Drive,
Caringbah, NSW 2229, Australia

Order No. AM1003970
ISBN 978-1-78038-278-4

Edited by Ruth Searle
Illustrated by Jon Burgerman
Designed by Lizzie Barrand

Printed in the EU

www.musicsales.com

Your Guarantee of Quality
As publishers, we strive to produce every book
to the highest commercial standards.
The music has been freshly engraved and the book has
been carefully designed to minimise awkward page turns
and to make playing from it a real pleasure.
Particular care has been given to specifying acid-free,
neutral-sized paper made from pulps which have not been
elemental chlorine bleached. This pulp is from farmed
sustainable forests and was produced with special regard
for the environment.
Throughout, the printing and binding have been planned
to ensure a sturdy, attractive publication which should
give years of enjoyment.
If your copy fails to meet our high standards,
please inform us and we will gladly replace it.

AMERICAN PATROL 18

BLUIN' THE BLUES 32

CANAL STREET BLUES 12

DOWN BY THE RIVERSIDE 6

A FOGGY DAY 26

FRANKIE AND JOHNNY 30

GO DOWN MOSES 9

I GOT RHYTHM 28

JUST A CLOSER WALK WITH THEE 5

LITTLE BROWN JUG 4

THE MAN I LOVE 13

MAPLE LEAF RAG 22

NOBODY KNOWS THE TROUBLE I'VE SEEN 8

PINETOP'S BOOGIE WOOGIE 24

SOLACE RAG 16

SWING LOW, SWEET CHARIOT 10

THEY CAN'T TAKE THAT AWAY FROM ME 20

WHEN THE SAINTS GO MARCHING IN 11

LITTLE BROWN JUG
TRADITIONAL

Light swing

My wife and I lived all a-lone in a lit-tle log hut we

call our own.__ She loved gin and I loved rum,

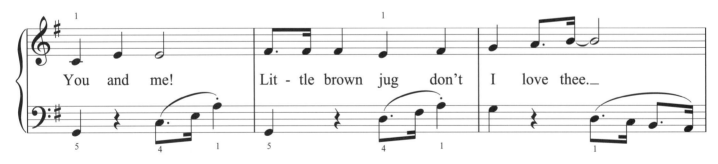

tell you what, don't we have fun! Ha ha ha!

You and me! Lit-tle brown jug don't I love thee.__

Ha ha ha ha ha! You and me! Oh,__ lit-tle brown jug don't I love thee!

JUST A CLOSER WALK WITH THEE
TRADITIONAL

Lazy swing

Just a clos - er walk with Thee, Je - sus grant my hum - ble plea. Dai - ly walk - ing close to Thee, let it be, dear Lord, let it be.

DOWN BY THE RIVERSIDE

TRADITIONAL

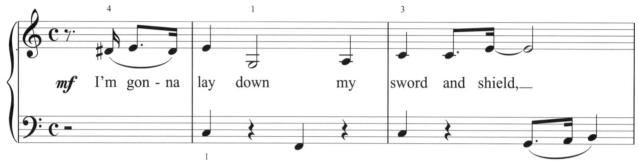

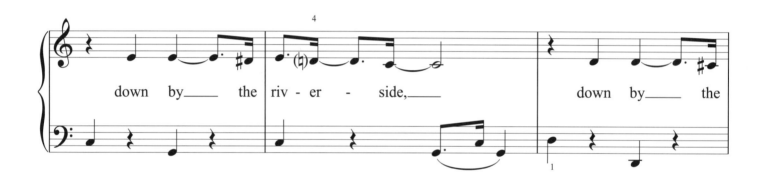

riv - er - side,__ gon-na stud - y war no more. I'm gon-na

stud - y war no more,__ I'm gon - na stud - y war no more,

__ I'm gon - na stud - y war no more. I'm gon - na

stud - y war no more,__ I'm gon - na stud - y war no more,__ I'm gon - na

stud - y war no more.

NOBODY KNOWS THE TROUBLE I'VE SEEN
TRADITIONAL

Fairly slow

No-bod - y knows the troub-le I've seen, no-bod - y knows but

*(last time **rit.**)*

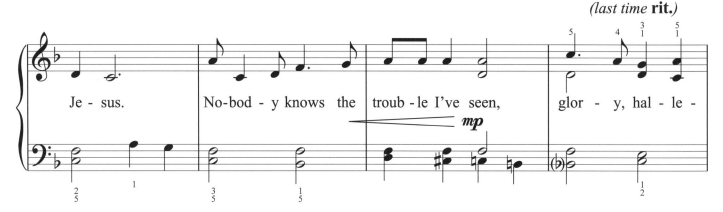

Je - sus. No-bod - y knows the troub-le I've seen, glor - y, hal - le -

moving on, slightly faster

- lu - jah! Some - times I'm up, some - times I'm down; oh, yes,

Fine

poco rit. **a tempo**

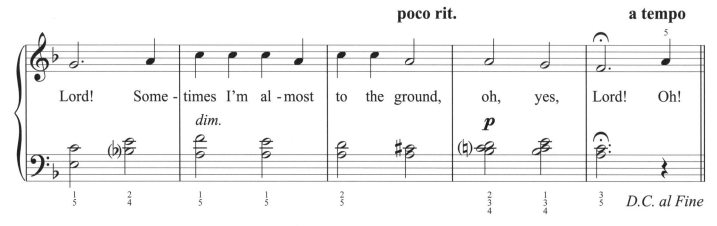

Lord! Some - times I'm al - most to the ground, oh, yes, Lord! Oh!

D.C. al Fine

GO DOWN MOSES
TRADITIONAL

Latin feel, not too fast

When Is - rael was in E - gypt's land, "Let my peo - ple go!"

Op - pressed so hard they could not stand,

"Let my peo - ple go!" Go down,

Mo - ses, way down in E - gypt's land; tell old

Phar - oah, "Let my peo - ple go!"

SWING LOW, SWEET CHARIOT
TRADITIONAL

Slowly

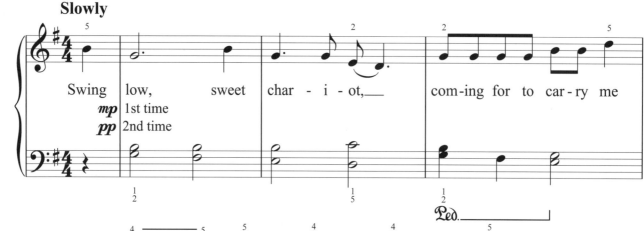

Swing low, sweet char - i - ot,___ com-ing for to car-ry me

mp 1st time
pp 2nd time

Ped.

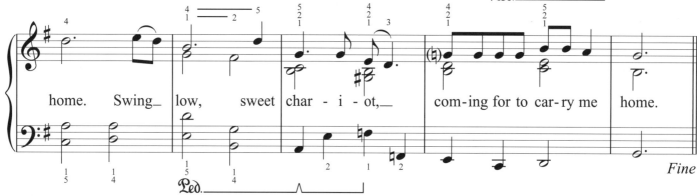

home. Swing_ low, sweet char - i - ot,___ com-ing for to car-ry me home.

Ped.

Fine

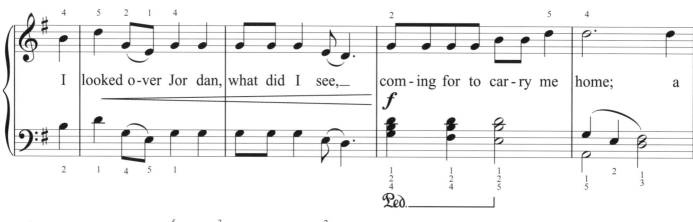

I looked o-ver Jor dan, what did I see,___ com-ing for to car-ry me home; a

f

Ped.

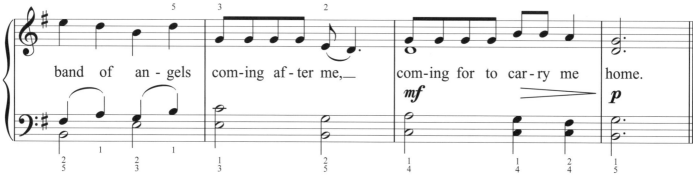

band of an - gels com-ing af-ter me,___ com-ing for to car-ry me home.

mf _____ *p*

D.C. al Fine

WHEN THE SAINTS GO MARCHING IN
TRADITIONAL

Lively

mf Oh, when the saints____ go march-ing in,____ oh, when the saints go march-ing in,____ I want to be____ in that num-ber,____ oh, when the saints go march-ing in.____

with soul

f

Oh, when the

in.____ *p*

CANAL STREET BLUES
MUSIC BY JOE 'KING' OLIVER

Fast dixieland

THE MAN I LOVE
MUSIC BY GEORGE GERSHWIN

Freely

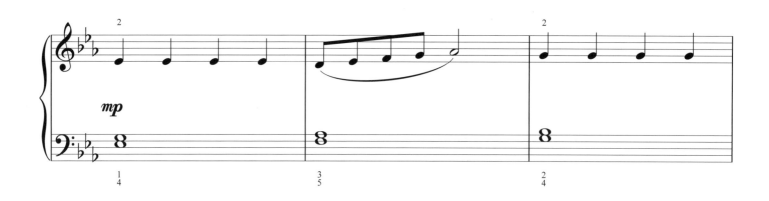

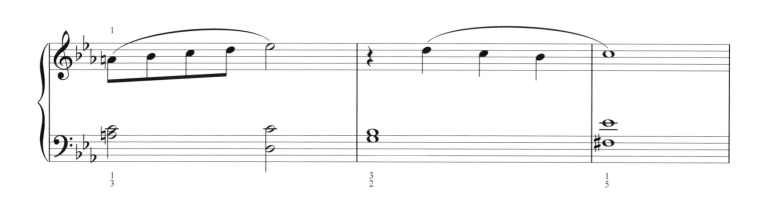

Ballad, gentle swing ♪. ♪ = ♪ ♪ (3)

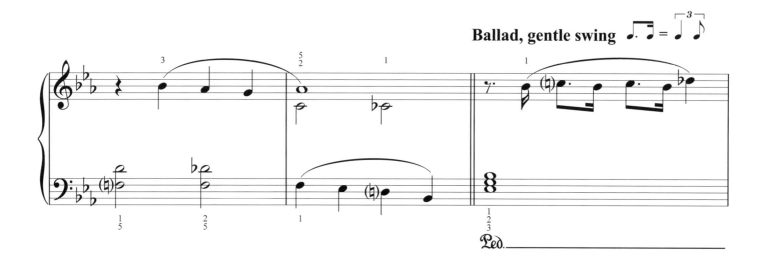

Ped.

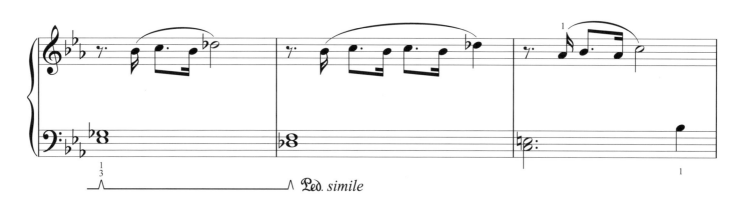

Ped. simile

SOLACE RAG
MUSIC BY SCOTT JOPLIN

Very slow march time

playfully

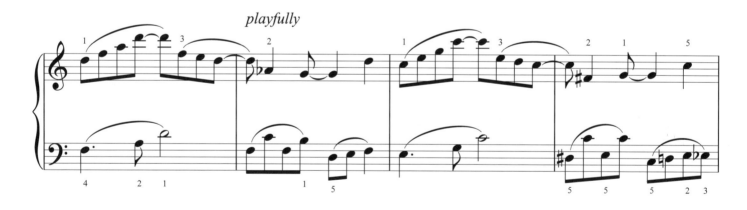

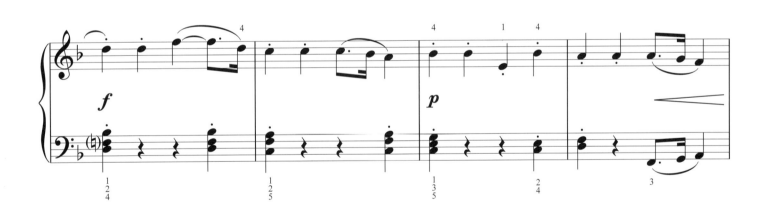

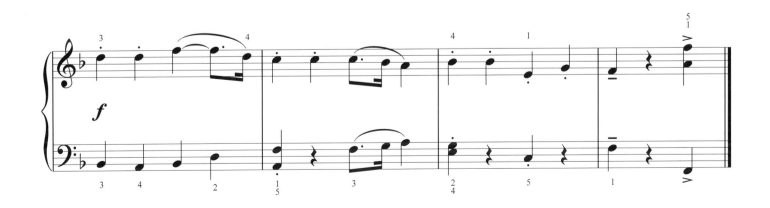

THEY CAN'T TAKE THAT AWAY FROM ME
MUSIC BY GEORGE GERSHWIN

Steady swing

MAPLE LEAF RAG
MUSIC BY SCOTT JOPLIN

Tempo di marcia

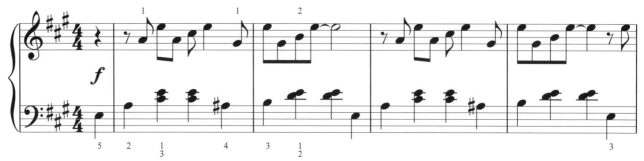

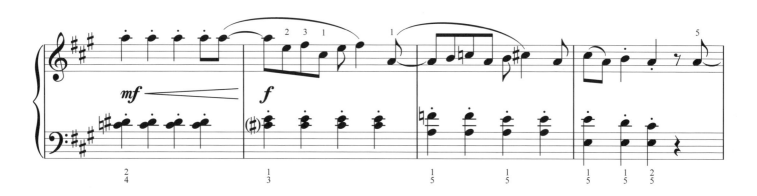

Fine

staccato

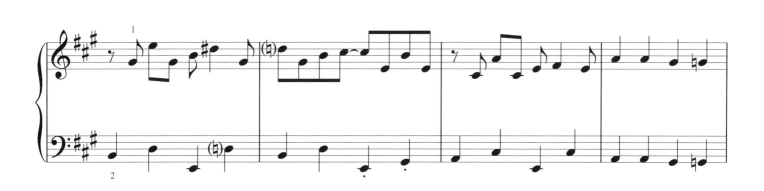

D.C. al Fine

PINE TOP'S BOOGIE WOOGIE
MUSIC BY SCOTT JOPLIN

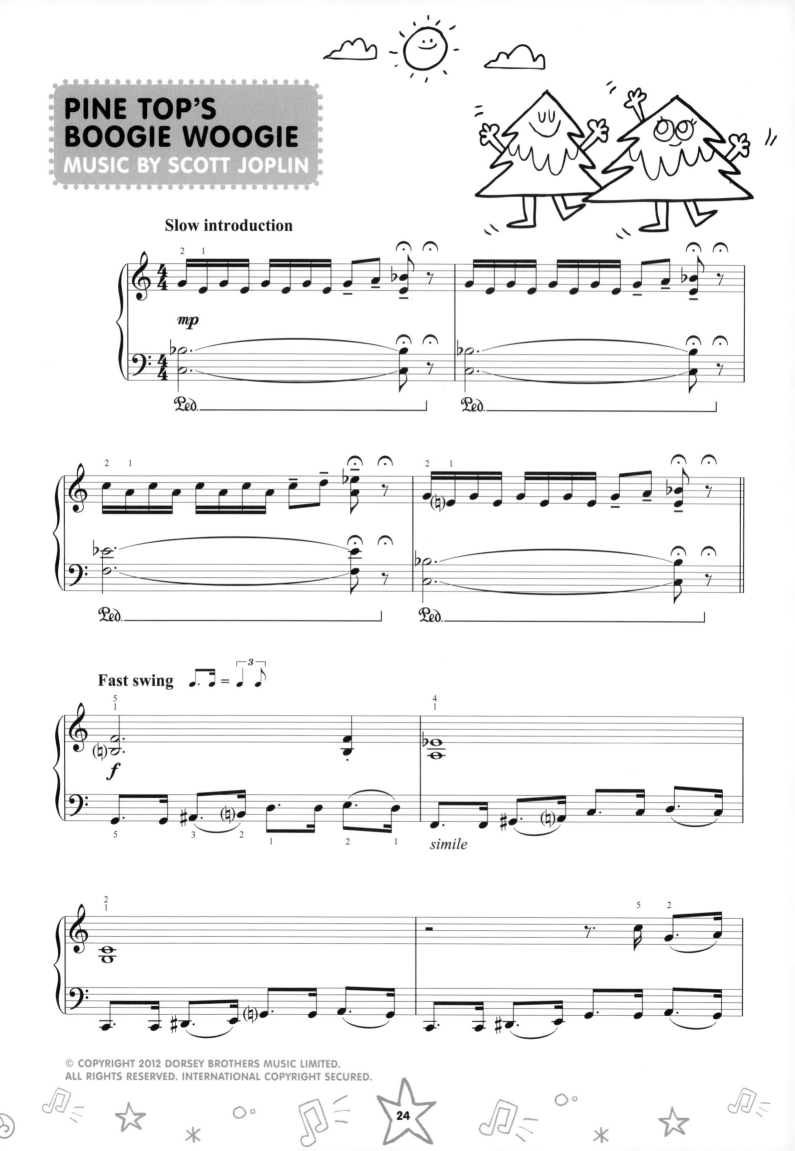

A FOGGY DAY

MUSIC BY GEORGE GERSHWIN

I GOT RHYTHM

MUSIC BY GEORGE GERSHWIN

Bright and upbeat

legato

FRANKIE AND JOHNNY
TRADITIONAL

BLUIN' THE BLUES
MUSIC BY W H RAGAS

Dixieland, lightly swung

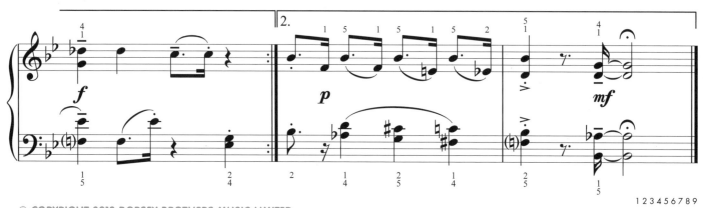

123456789